Introduction

My friend and colleague Michelle Madder devised this key signature table **during** a class one day! It just so happened that while explaining how many sharps or flats were in each key, a pattern emerged.

There are many different key signature tables around, but I believe this table is the simplest to write down and the easiest to understand. Music is a magnificently mathematical language!

Many thanks to Michelle for her support in releasing this publication.

Samantha Coates
Author, BlitzBooks

Published by
Chester Music,
part of The Music Sales Group,
14-15 Berners Street,
London W1T 3LJ, UK.

Exclusive Distributors:
Music Sales Limited
Distribution Centre, Newmarket Road,
Bury St Edmunds, Suffolk IP33 3YB, UK.

Music Sales Pty Limited
4th floor, Lisgar House,
30-32 Carrington Street,
Sydney, NSW 2000, Australia.

Order No. CH85217
ISBN 978-1-78558-360-5
This book © Copyright 2016 Chester Music Limited,
a division of Music Sales Limited.

Printed in the EU.
www.musicsales.com

Your Guarant‹

As publishers, we strive to p‹‹‹‹‹‹‹‹ ‹‹‹‹‹
book to the highest commercial standards.

Particular care has been given to specifying acid-free, neutral-sized paper made from pulps which have not been elemental chlorine bleached. This pulp is from farmed sustainable forests and was produced with special regard for the environment.

Throughout, the printing and binding have been planned to ensure a sturdy, attractive publication which should give years of enjoyment.

If your copy fails to meet our high standards, please inform us and we will gladly replace it.

Chester Music
part of The Music Sales Group
London / New York / Paris / Sydney / Copenhagen /
Berlin / Madrid / Hong Kong / Tokyo

The Blitz Key Signature Table

♯ major

F♯	C(♯)	G	D	A	E	B
6	0(7)	1	2	3	4	5

♯ minor

F♯	C♯	G♯	D♯	A(♯)	E	B
3	4	5	6	0(7)	1	2

♭ major

B♭	E♭	A♭	D♭	G♭	C(♭)	F
2	3	4	5	6	0(7)	1

♭ minor

B♭	E♭	A(♭)	D	G	C	F
5	6	0(7)	1	2	3	4

How to Read the Table

* ★ The numbers beneath each letter name tell you how many sharps or flats are in that key

* ★ The reason for the brackets around the number 7 is that C major has no sharps but C **sharp** major has seven sharps. The same goes for A minor and A flat minor.

* ★ To find the relative major or minor of any key, simply look for the corresponding numbers

* ★ There are no catches or exceptions to this table. Once you know how to read it, you can't go wrong!

Quick Quiz

1. What is the key signature of D flat major?

2. What is the key signature of A sharp minor?

3. Which two keys share the key signature of six flats?

4. What is the relative major of F sharp minor?

5. What is the highest number of sharps or flats in any key?

Step One: Sharp Major

First, write down the order of the sharps:

F   C   G   ____   ____   ____   ____

(N.B. My favourite sentence for remembering the order of the sharps is 'Fat Cat Goes Driving And Eats Bananas'... check out www.blitzbooks.com for more great ideas!)

Which major key has no sharps?

_____

So, write **0** under the C. Now start numbering the others: **1** under the G, **2** under the D and so on.

For the number **6**, you'll have to go back to the beginning of the line. This is the most important part... whenever you go back to the beginning of the line, you MUST write little sharp signs next to the letters. F major does not have six sharps; F **sharp** major has six sharps!

The C already has a **0**, but write a **7** in brackets and a sharp in brackets to show that C sharp major has seven sharps.

Now check to see if this looks the same as page 2!

Now practise writing out the first part of your key signature table!

♯ major _____

♯ major _____

♯ major _____

Step Two: Sharp Minor

Write the order of sharps again (remember, it's minor now, but still sharps).

____   ____   ____   ____   ____   ____   ____

Now, which minor key has no sharps?

_____

So, write **0** under the A, **1** under the E and so on.

What must you do when you go back to the beginning of the line? Add _____ signs to the letters.

The A already has a **0**, but add a **7** in brackets and a sharp in brackets to show that A sharp major has seven sharps.

Check now with page 2!

Let's practise the second part of the key signature table...

♯ minor ▬▬▬▬▬▬▬▬▬▬▬▬▬▬▬▬▬▬

♯ minor ▬▬▬▬▬▬▬▬▬▬▬▬▬▬▬▬▬▬

♯ minor ▬▬▬▬▬▬▬▬▬▬▬▬▬▬▬▬▬▬

Step Three: Flat Major

It's now time to switch to writing the order of the flats, which is simply the order of the sharps backwards!

B E A ___ ___ ___ ___

Which major key has no flats?

_____

So, write **0** under the C. Now start numbering the others: **1** under the F then for the number **2**, you'll have to go back to the beginning of the line. This is the most important part... whenever you go back to the beginning of the line, you MUST write little flat signs next to the letters. B major does not have two flats; B flat major has two flats!

The C already has a **0**, but write a **7** in brackets and a flat in brackets to show that C flat major has seven flats.

Now check to see if this looks the same as page 2!

Time to practise writing out the third part of your key signature table...

♭ major ▬▬▬▬▬▬▬▬▬▬▬▬▬▬▬▬▬▬▬▬▬▬▬▬

♭ major ▬▬▬▬▬▬▬▬▬▬▬▬▬▬▬▬▬▬▬▬▬▬▬▬

♭ major ▬▬▬▬▬▬▬▬▬▬▬▬▬▬▬▬▬▬▬▬▬▬▬▬

Step Four: Flat Minor

←――――――――――――――――――――→

Write the order of flats again (remember, it's minor now, but still flats).

___   ___   ___   ___   ___   ___   ___

Now, which minor key has no flats?

_____

So, write **0** under the A, **1** under the D and so on.

What must you do when you go back to the beginning of the line? Add _____ signs to the letters.

The A already has a **0**, but add a **7** in brackets and a flat in brackets to show that A flat major has seven flats.

Check now with page 2!

And finally, let's practise the last part of your key signature table!

♭ minor ▨▨▨▨▨▨▨▨▨▨▨▨▨▨▨▨▨▨▨▨▨▨▨▨▨▨▨▨▨

♭ minor ▨▨▨▨▨▨▨▨▨▨▨▨▨▨▨▨▨▨▨▨▨▨▨▨▨▨▨▨▨

♭ minor ▨▨▨▨▨▨▨▨▨▨▨▨▨▨▨▨▨▨▨▨▨▨▨▨▨▨▨▨▨

How to Write Out the Table

Things to remember:

★ You must set the table out under four headings:

♯ major

♯ minor

♭ major

♭ minor

★ You must write the order of the sharps for the sharp headings

★ You must write the order of the flats for the flat headings

★ Remember, the idea is that you will start writing out this table at the beginning of your exam. It is extremely important to write it out quickly and CORRECTLY!!!

WARNING: The most common mistake is to accidentally write the order of sharps for **major** followed by the order of flats for **minor** on the next line. Be very careful not to do this!

Write out the Blitz Key Signature Table as quickly as you can on the next few pages.

Get someone to time you or you can time yourself. Write your time in the box, and then check your table against page 2. You must add on 10 seconds for each mistake you find!

Hopefully with practice you will be able to write it out in less than two minutes without any mistakes.

REMEMBER: the most important thing is to write out the table **correctly** — you will be referring to it a lot!

Time:

Time:

Time: